# Adam & Eve

MB
MACAW
BOOKS

# Adam & Eve

© 2009 Macaw Books (U.S.A.)

Published by:
**Macaw Books (U.S.A.)**
www.macawbooks.com

First Published 2009

Edited by Linda O'Brien

Printed in India

IN THE BEGINNING GOD CREATED THE HEAVEN AND THE EARTH. BUT THE EARTH WAS EMPTY AND COVERED WITH DARKNESS.

LET THERE BE LIGHT!

WHEN THE EARTH WAS FILLED WITH LIGHT, GOD DIVIDED IT INTO DAY AND NIGHT. THEN, HE COVERED THE EARTH IN A BEAUTIFUL BLUE BLANKET.

THE EARTH LOOKS GOOD, BUT NEEDS TO BE A LITTLE MORE ORGANIZED.

IT WAS THEN THAT HE SEPARATED THE EARTH'S SURFACE INTO DRY LAND AND WATER. SO, THE VAST LAND MASSES AND SEAS WERE FORMED.

ADAM AND EVE WERE, MEANWHILE, WERE UNAWARE OF THE IMPOSTOR AND CARRIED OUT THEIR DAILY CHORES.

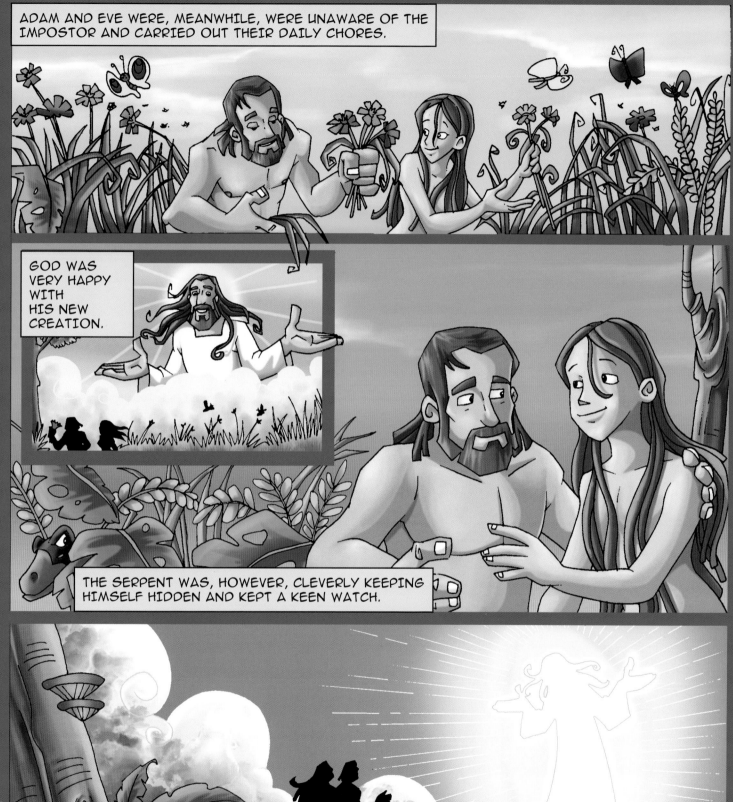

GOD WAS VERY HAPPY WITH HIS NEW CREATION.

THE SERPENT WAS, HOWEVER, CLEVERLY KEEPING HIMSELF HIDDEN AND KEPT A KEEN WATCH.

HE FOLLOWED EVERY ACTIVITY OF ADAM AND EVE AND EVEN LISTENED TO WHAT GOD TOLD THEM TIME AND AGAIN.

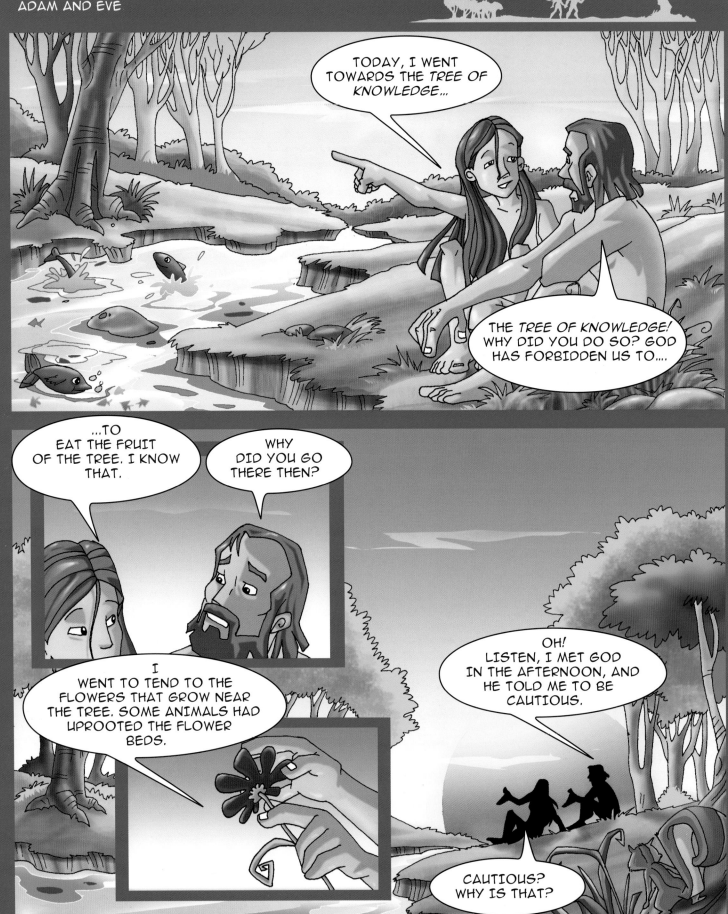

A FEW DAYS LATER, ADAM AND EVE WERE WORKING IN THE GARDEN, SOWING SOME SEEDS.

THE AREA WHERE WE HAVE TO SOW SEEDS IS QUITE LARGE. IT WILL TAKE MANY DAYS TO SOW THEM.

WHY DON'T WE DIVIDE OUR TASKS TO COMPLETE IT EARLY?

DIVIDE OUR TASKS? DO YOU NOT REMEMBER WHAT I TOLD YOU?

OF COURSE I REMEMBER WHAT YOU TOLD ME.

THEN HOW CAN YOU SUGGEST SOMETHING LIKE THAT?

LISTEN, IF WE DIVIDE OUR TASKS THEN WE CAN TAKE CARE OF THE GARDEN PROPERLY.

BUT THAT CAN ALSO BE DONE IF WE WORK TOGETHER.

GOD HAS NOT SAID THAT WE CAN'T DIVIDE OUR WORK! WE CAN STILL BE CAUTIOUS IF WE WORK SEPARATELY.

ADAM THOUGHT FOR A WHILE.

YOU SAY THAT YOU WILL BE CAUTIOUS.

YES, I WILL.

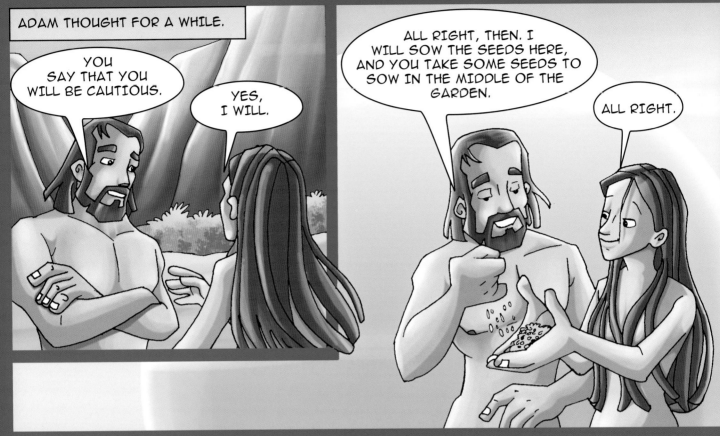

ALL RIGHT, THEN. I WILL SOW THE SEEDS HERE, AND YOU TAKE SOME SEEDS TO SOW IN THE MIDDLE OF THE GARDEN.

ALL RIGHT.

THUS ADAM AND EVE DECIDED TO SEPARATE TO WORK EFFICIENTLY, LITTLE KNOWING WHAT WAS AWAITING THEM...

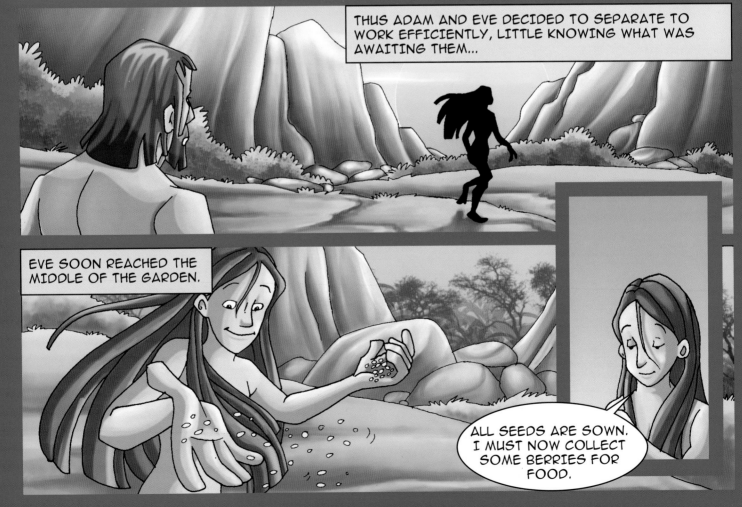

EVE SOON REACHED THE MIDDLE OF THE GARDEN.

ALL SEEDS ARE SOWN. I MUST NOW COLLECT SOME BERRIES FOR FOOD.

THE NEXT MOMENT...

ADAM! WHY ARE YOU HIDING FROM ME? YOU LOOK AFRAID! HAVE YOU EATEN THE FORBIDDEN FRUIT?

EVE MADE ME EAT THE FORBIDDEN FRUIT.

IT WAS THE SERPENT! HE MADE ME EAT IT.

GOD WAS FILLED WITH ANGER AS WELL AS HURT...

YOUR DISOBEDIENCE WILL BE PUNISHED. SERPENT, YOU ARE CURSED TO ALWAYS CRAWL ON THE GROUND. THE CHILDREN OF MAN WILL BE YOUR ENEMY, AND AT HIS HANDS YOU WILL DIE.

EVE, FOR THE SIN YOU HAVE COMMITED, YOU'LL HAVE TO BEAR PAIN WHILE GIVING BIRTH TO YOUR CHILDREN.

ADAM, YOU WILL HAVE TO WORK HARD FOR A LIVING. YOU WILL GROW YOUR OWN FOOD AND LEAD A LIFE FULL OF LABOR.

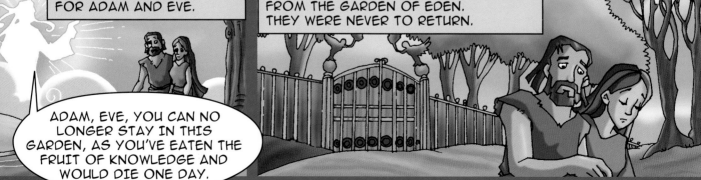

GOD THEN MADE CLOTHES FOR ADAM AND EVE.

THUS, ADAM AND EVE WERE BANISHED FROM THE GARDEN OF EDEN. THEY WERE NEVER TO RETURN.

ADAM, EVE, YOU CAN NO LONGER STAY IN THIS GARDEN, AS YOU'VE EATEN THE FRUIT OF KNOWLEDGE AND WOULD DIE ONE DAY.

## UN-JUMBLE THESE WORDS FROM THE STORY

1.  MDAA

2.  NHISAB

3.  ERCNTIAO

4.  DRESSANK

5.  IEODYBS

6.  DDBENIFRO

7.  IFTUR

8.  ADEGRN

9.  EVNHEA

10. OSTIMPRO

11. DWKNOLGEE

12. TANSA

13. EESSD

14. PSNTERE

## CHOOSE THE RIGHT ANSWER

1. IN THE BEGINNING THERE WAS:

   A. DARKNESS
   B. LIGHT
   C. WATER

2. GOD CREATED EVE FROM:

   A. MUD
   B. A RIB OF ADAM
   C. FLOWERS

3. GOD FORBADE ADAM AND EVE TO:

   A. LOOK AT THE TREE OF KNOWLEDGE
   B. EAT FROM THE TREE OF KNOWLEDGE
   C. TOUCH THE TREE OF KNOWLEDGE

4. WHO PERSUADED EVE TO EAT FROM THE TREE OF KNOWLEDGE?

   A. ADAM
   B. LION
   C. SERPENT

5. AS A PUNISHMENT FOR THEIR DISOBEDIENCE, GOD...

   A. BANISHED ADAM AND EVE FROM THE GARDEN OF EDEN
   B. IMPRISONED ADAM AND EVE
   C. SEPARATED THEM FROM ONE ANOTHER

ANSWERS: 1A, 2B, 3B, 4C, 5A